Winnie-the-Pooh's

50 things
to do
before
you're
5 ³⁄₄

EGMONT
We bring stories to life

First published in Great Britain in 2018 by Egmont UK Limited,
The Yellow Building, 1 Nicholas Road, London W11 4AN

www.egmont.co.uk

© 2018 Disney Enterprises, Inc
Based on the 'Winnie-the-Pooh' works by A.A.Milne and E.H.Shepard
Text by A.A.Milne copyright © Trustees of the Pooh Properties
Line illustrations copyright © E.H.Shepard
Additional decorations by Andrew Grey
Written by Chloë Boyes
Designed by Jeannette O'Toole and Pritty Ramjee

ISBN 978 1 4052 8953 5
68471/1
Printed in China

Adult supervision is recommended when glue, paint, scissors and
other sharp points are in use.

Stay safe online. Egmont is not responsible for content
hosted by third parties.

Acknowledgments

Dreamstime.com

ID 84985196 © Adam Wesolowski, p. 30-31; ID 23058434 © Alekss, p. 69; ID 74318054 © Alexandrum01, p. 32; ID 17852218 © Anest, p. 28;
ID 73435369 © Anna Ileysh, p. 18; ID 77979496 © Antonel, p. 15; ID 56725842 © Aperturesound, p. 64; ID 17597145 © Brian Kushner, p. 49;
ID 10249061 © Briancweed, p. 78-79; ID 73895442 © Chanin Wardkhian, p. 64; ID 24595530 © Christian Jung, p. 46-47;
ID 34879869 © Dimitar Marinov, p. 6, 9, 69, 76, 79; ID 33427159 © Dragonimages, p. 33; ID 10908006 © Eaniton, p. 60;
ID 16042770 © Elena Elisseeva, ID 501784 © Elena Elisseeva, p. 46-47; ID 93257689 © Elena Nichizhenova, p. 65;
ID 76725044 © Elizabeth Cummings, p. 24, 26; ID 56320125 © Etiennevoss, p. 64; ID 46372716 © Exopixel, p. 7, 11, 68, 77, 78;
ID 63699820 © Flas100, p. 68-69; ID 51507257 © Foto821, p. 15, 69; ID 92312211 © Furo_felix, p. 19, 68; ID 72651328 © Gavran333, p. 24;
ID 29214117 © Godfer, p. 38; ID 34788573 © Gryzeva, p. 15, 69; ID 13044672 © Inga Nielsen, p. 50; ID 45254322 © Insago2012, p. 76-77;
ID 6153594 © Iryna Sosnytska, p. 78-79; ID 74978167 © Jefunne Gimpel, p. 13; ID 5310885 © Jhogan, p. 30; ID 40819980 © Kamolrat, p. 36-37;
ID 62878073 © Karayuschij, p. 24; ID 82147904 © Katarinagondova, p. 53; ID 64162211 © Ksushsh, p. 15, 34, 54-55;
ID 32573530 © Lavoview, p. 50; ID 45600536 © Maart, p. 50; ID 64524349 © Marina473, p. 26;
ID 6/689348 © Martin Novak, p. 22; ID 66207017 © Maryna Kulchytska, p. 40; ID 31615200 © Michael Mill, p. 25;
ID 32098811 © Mikelane45, p. 25; ID 14031753 © Mladen Bozickovic, p. 21; ID 54961663, ID 59775714,
ID 15685767 © Monkey Business Images, p. 42, 54-55, 73; ID 56327809 © Nataliya Arzamasova, p. 33; ID 20924262 © Natespics, p. 52;
ID 72425047 © Nipaporn Panyacharoen, p. 13, 16, 34, 69; ID 6215253 © Norman Chan, p. 26; ID 93240562 © Nunthana Setila, p. 30;
ID 33416578 © Olga Voronishcheva, p. 44; ID 17912789 © Pavel Bugrov, p. 26; ID 58338549 © Petar Dojkic, p. 62;
ID 54581995 © Philip Kinsey, p. 46-47; ID 20390102 © Philip Waring, p. 22; ID 33893785 © Photographerlondon, p. 12, 72;
ID 53339515 © Pioneer111, p. 7, 39-40; ID 98289768 © Priya Kumrueang, p. 64; ID 81264679 © Reinis Bigacs, p. 64;
ID 77339206 © Ruslanchik, p. 7, 13, 15, 19, 69; ID 26617794 © Ruud Morijn, p. 25; ID 25527781 © Santos06, p. 62; ID 39438052 © Sanyals p. 13;
ID 60145275 © Sarah Marchant, p. 24; ID 51261009 © Scriptx, p. 26; ID 28192314 © Sergii Kolesnyk, p. 46-47;
ID 49394415, 37177824 © Sgoodwin4813, p. 7, 13; ID 21814389 © Slallison, p. 47; ID 13061170 © Soare Cecilia, p. 33;
ID 56796657 © Sommai Sommai, p. 15; ID 87806531 © Smileus, p. 10; ID 39559980 © Stryjek, p. 46-47;
ID 58370385 © Supparsorn Wantarnagon, p. 40, 69; ID 51756470 © Swkunst, p. 6, 84141690 © Tinnakorn Srivichai, p. 53;
ID 55529424 © Toni Genes, p. 34; ID 44403157 © Tracy Decourcy, p. 65; Unknown, p. 20; ID 19298768 © wabeno, p. 26;
ID 99034547 © Walentain2012, p. 20; ID 86287258 © Yotrak, p. 64; ID 41660279 © Zdravinjo, p. 36-37; ID 7194175 © Zts , p. 24

Shutterstock.com

RaSveta, p. 14; MNStudio, p. 19; Kryzhov, p. 57

Winnie-the-Pooh's
50 things
to do
before
you're
5 ¾

EGMONT

Health and safety

Adult supervision will be required for a number of the many adventurous activities described in this book. Where relevant, the activity will be flagged at the top of the page and within the activity.

Adult supervision is recommended when glue, paint, scissors and any other sharp points are in use. Wear protective clothing and cover surfaces to avoid staining.

The
**outdoor
adventures**
of

..........*everyone*..........

...*reading this!*...

Contents

Tick ✔ each task when you have done it.

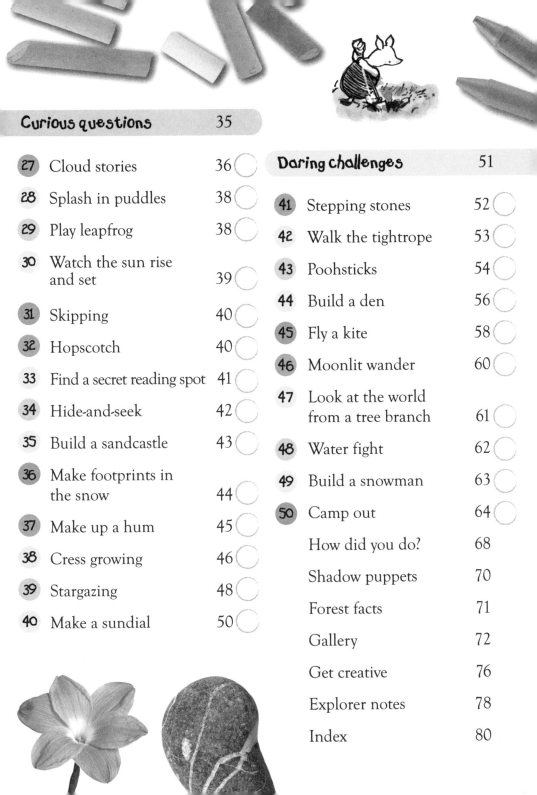

All things arty

'Without Pooh,' said Rabbit solemnly as he sharpened his pencil, 'the adventure would be impossible.'

1 Leaf drawing

Find an interesting-looking leaf.

Trace around your leaf and colour it in, then find a different shaped leaf and do the same.

Keep going until you have a piece of paper full of leafy patterns.

OAK

HOLLY

HORSE CHESTNUT

BEECH

2 Trunk patterns

Take a piece of paper and a wax crayon (or piece of chalk) to a tree. Place your sheet of paper against the trunk and roll your crayon over the paper.

You will see the pattern of the tree trunk on your paper.

Try this on different varieties of tree and see how the bark patterns change.

Check out page 71 for fun facts about the forest!

3 Daisy chains

First, pick your flowers – be sure to pick daisies with long, thick stems. Using your fingernail, (a grown-up can help you with this) make a slit down the stem of each daisy, to make a loop.

Once you have a few ready, you can start to thread them together into your chain. It's up to you whether you make a short or a long chain – maybe you could make a bracelet or a headdress.

4 Forest in a bottle

You can use twigs, moss, flowers, grass, pebbles, sand, leaves and anything else you find as you explore the outdoors. Place all of your forest items in a plastic bottle and keep it on display in your room, to remind you of all your adventures.

5 Spell with sticks

Can you write your name using twigs and sticks?

⑥ Fingerprint animals

To make your animals,
dip your fingertips in paint and
place firmly onto your paper.

Make a row of prints for
the perfect caterpillar and four in
a square for a pretty butterfly.

Once your prints are dry,
you can use pens and pencils
to add details such as eyes,
hair and whiskers.

Tree monsters

Start by smoothing mud onto the surface of a tree trunk to make the face shape. Add stones or pebbles for the eyes, nose and ears of your monster.

Now, give your monster its own personality with twigs, leaves and moss for hair, a mouth and other features. Does your monster have a beard? Or a crown of sticks?

Take a picture of your monster and stick it on pages 72 or 73 with all your other crafts!

8 Forest potions

To create your own forest potion, use mud or water as your base.

Gather flowers, leaves, pebbles and grass and grind your ingredients between two big stones. Use a stick to stir your potion.

Mix all of your ingredients together in a plastic bottle and your potion will be complete!

What spell will your potion cast? Does it have a name?

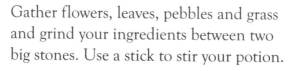

There lives an old man at the top of the street,
And the end of his beard reaches down to his feet,
He has worked all his life (and he's terribly old)
At a wonderful spell which says, 'Lo and behold!'

PLEASE REMEMBER: Your potion is not for consumption!

9 Stamp making

Recreate the shapes you see outside by making potato stamps. You will need the help of an adult to cut your potato in half.

Draw the shape you would like. It could be a leaf, a flower or even a paw print. Then ask an adult to carve around your design. Allow the potato to dry out a little and you're ready to dip in paint and start stamping!

Flower pressing

10

Pick a flower – check the petals and pull out any which have started to go brown.

Place your flower between two sheets of kitchen roll and weigh down with a heavy book. Leave for 10 days before checking.

11 Pebble pets

Collect round, flat pebbles or stones.

Use paint to draw the pattern of your pet's coat and permanent marker for eyes, a nose and a mouth.

If you have scraps of felt or wool, you could use them to make ears, whiskers, tails or antennae. Ask an adult to help you as you will need strong glue.

Use tweezers to put the features into place. Once the paint and glue have dried, your pet is ready for a new home. You could use an old matchbox to keep them safe.

12 Pine cone decorations

Set out bowls with different coloured paint and dip one end of each pine cone in a different colour. When dry, place all of the cones in a bowl and you'll have a rainbow display for your room.

If you don't have a bowl, ask an adult to help you glue ribbon to the base of each and hang them in window frames.

If you want to make your pine cones festive, mix water and PVA glue, roll the cones so they are lightly covered and then roll them in glitter. When they have dried, add ribbon to them and you'll have perfect decorations.

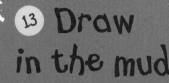

13 Draw in the mud

Find a sturdy-looking stick and use this to make marks in the mud. Draw pictures or write your name. Take a picture and stick it on pages 72 and 73.

14 Shadow puppets

Draw your shapes on paper, first with pencil and then with b
marker to stop the light getting through. There
are templates for you to trace on page 70.

Attach sticks to one side of the
template so you can control your
characters. Hold them up to a plain
wall or sheet with your torch or bonfire
behind. You will be able to see your
shapes as shadows in the light.

Use your silhouettes to
tell stories of the
adventures Christopher
Robin and his friends
have in the Hundred
Acre Wood.

Jack's Favorite

15 Make static electricity

Rub a balloon on a woolly jumper. This will build up an electric charge on the balloon's surface. Now hold the balloon near your head and watch as your hair stands up on end!

Nobody can be **uncheered** *with a* **balloon.**

Beastly adventures

'Tracks,' said Piglet. 'Pawmarks.' He gave a little squeak of excitement. 'Oh Pooh! Do you think it's a – a – a Woozle?'

16 Feed the birds

Attract birds to your garden or local park by making them tasty snacks.

oats

raisins

breadcrumbs

grated cheese

Mix wild bird seed with oats, raisins, breadcrumbs and grated cheese. Ask an adult to help you melt suet or lard and using a ratio of 2-parts fat to 1-part grain, mix everything together.

Use a hollowed out orange, an old yogurt pot or the bottom of an empty bottle to hold your bird feed. Make sure you get an adult to help when using scissors or sharp points.

17 Catch a Heffalump

When looking for Heffalumps, Pooh and Piglet know that
tracks are a good place to start. Search in your garden, at the
park or in woodlands and see if you can spot any tracks.
Do you know which type of animal made them?

FOX

DEER

BADGER

Draw the tracks you
find on pages 74 and 75.

Bounce like Tigger

18

Tigger loves to bounce. See if you can bounce up and down like Tigger.

Feed the ducks

19

Make sure you are with an adult!

When you visit lakes, canals, rivers or the park remember to take along food to feed the ducks. Here are some tasty, healthy snacks for your feathered friends:

sweetcorn

lettuce

rice

peas

seeds

oats

26

20 Animal baby spotting

Discover the names of animal babies as you explore the outdoors. Tick each animal you spot and draw any others you find.

Chick

Lamb

Puppy

Foal

Kit

First came Christopher Robin and Rabbit, then Piglet and Pooh; then Kanga, with Roo in her pocket ... all Rabbit's friends-and-relations.

21 Watch a caterpillar transform

Search for caterpillars on leaves near long grass and wildflowers.

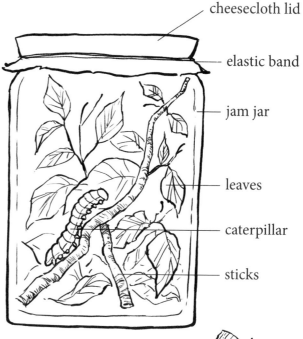

cheesecloth lid

elastic band

jam jar

leaves

caterpillar

sticks

Caterpillars can be fussy. You will need to give them leaves from the same plant you found them on. Make sure the leaves are always fresh and take out any that are dry or brown.

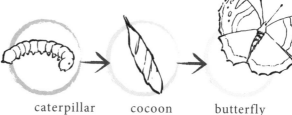

caterpillar   cocoon   butterfly

Once your caterpillar is fully grown, they will form a cocoon and become a chrysalis. Keep watch, as your butterfly is nearly here! Once the butterfly emerges and its wings have expanded, let it out to fly freely in the wild.

22 Raise a ladybird

Use a plastic container to make your ladybird's house. Poke holes in the lid and place a damp paper towel inside, for humidity.

Search for ladybirds in bushes and gently shake the leaf that they're sitting on so they fall into their new home.

For food, soak a cotton ball in a mixture of honey and water. You can also add tiny bits of fruit for them to feast on. Make sure to replace the food after a few days so it doesn't rot.

Keep your ladybird house in the shade and make sure to set them free after a few days!

23

Search for a beetle

Beetles and other insects like to live under stones, logs and tree stumps. See how many you can find.

I found a little beetle,
so that Beetle was his name.

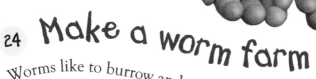

24 Make a worm farm

Worms like to burrow and explore in the safety of the soil. To watch some worms at work, you can make your own worm farm.

Use a big plastic container (make sure it's clear, so that you can check how your worms are getting on). Give your worms air holes in the top and drainage holes in the bottom.

Add bedding, made from a mixture of soil and sand, so that the worms can burrow and explore.

You can feed them leftovers, but avoid meat or dairy. They like fruit and vegetables best.

Gather your worms from the surface of the soil (they often appear after it's been raining).

Worms prefer the dark, so keep your farm in a cupboard or covered to keep the light out.

Add holes in
the top for air

food

sand

soil

sand

soil

Add air holes
at the bottom
for drainage

25 Teddy bears' picnic

To hold your own teddy bears' picnic, invite your friends over and ask them to bring their favourite teddy with them. You will need a blanket in a shady spot out of the sun as well as paper plates and cups for everyone. Be sure to have enough for your friends *and* their bears.

Choose snacks for your friends to eat – do they like honey, like Pooh? Or would they prefer sandwiches? Don't forget something refreshing to drink, too.

'Nearly eleven o'clock,'
said Pooh happily.
'You're just in time for a little
smackerel of something.'

Once you've finished,
remember to put all of your
rubbish in a bin and leave the
area as you found it.

26 Build a nest

There was Eeyore's house, looking as comfy as anything.
'[It has an] inside as well as outside,' said Pooh proudly.

For lots of birds, nests make a good home and the perfect place to lay their eggs.

See if you can build a nest from the things you find outside.

Moss, twigs, grasses, mud and stems can all be used. Twist and weave your nest together, adding one thing at a time.

Once your nest is finished, take a picture of it for your photo gallery.

34

Curious questions

I've got shoes with grown-up laces,
I've got knickers and a pair of braces,
I'm all ready to run some races.
Who's coming
out with me?

27 Cloud stories

How sweet to be a Cloud
Floating in the Blue!

Every little cloud
Always sings aloud.

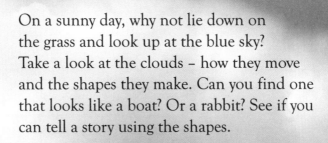

On a sunny day, why not lie down on the grass and look up at the blue sky? Take a look at the clouds – how they move and the shapes they make. Can you find one that looks like a boat? Or a rabbit? See if you can tell a story using the shapes.

28 Splash in puddles

John had Great Big Waterproof Boots on; John had a Great Big Waterproof Hat; John had a Great Big Waterproof Mackintosh – And that (Said John) Is That.

Have you ever splashed in puddles? Next time it's raining, put on your Great Big Waterproof Boots and jump!

29 Play leapfrog

One person (the lilypad) crouches low on the floor, tucking their arms and head in.

The other person (the frog) runs and springs over them by placing their hands on the lilypad's back.

Take it in turns being the lilypad and the frog!

Frogs have very long back legs, which bend and spring them forwards with a hop!

30

Watch the sun rise and set

As the sun rises in the morning and sets in the evening it can create beautiful colours across the sky.

To watch the sun rise or set, pick a clear day. Try to find a hill with a good view of the landscape as this will allow you to watch it for as long as possible.

Take some coloured chalk with you and draw a picture of the different shades of the sun as it rises or sets, blending in the layers to recreate the sky.

Make sure you are with an adult!

39

31 Skipping

Christopher Robin goes
Hoppity, hoppity,
Hoppity, hoppity, hop.
Whenever I tell him
Politely to stop it, he
Says he can't possibly stop.

Grab a skipping rope and start hopping! Skip on your own, in pairs or as a group.

32 Hopscotch

You will need chalk or masking tape to mark your hopscotch grid.

Take it in turns to hop from square to square.

Each player needs a token (use shells, coins or buttons) and before their turn, they should throw the token onto the squares (player 1 throws to square 1, player 2 to 2 etc.).

Players must hop over any square with a token on.

You're out if you hop on a square with a token or if you put two feet on one square.

33 Find a secret reading spot

Take your favourite story and find a secret reading hideout. This could be somewhere in your room, on an enormous pile of cushions, under the stairs or outside in the garden.

Take time by yourself to look at the pictures in your book, or maybe make up your own tales of adventure.

41

34

Hide-and-seek

While the seeker counts from 1 to 20, everyone else must hide.

Once the seeker reaches 20, they must find the other players, so choose your hiding place well!

The last person to be found is the winner and becomes the seeker in the next game.

The Search for Small was still going on all over the Forest.

35 Build a sandcastle

Put damp sand in a bucket and press it down firmly with your fists.

Turn the bucket over onto the sand, tap the bucket and lift.

Collect shells and pebbles to decorate your castle and make windows and doors.

You could also dig out a moat to protect your sandcastle from enemies!

We had sand in the eyes and the ears and the nose,
And sand in the hair, and sand-between-the-toes.

36 Make footprints in the snow

*Piglet was wearing a white muffler round his neck and feeling more **snowy** behind the ears than he had **ever** felt before.*

If it has been snowing, put on your wellies and try to make footprints in the snow. Listen to the crunch your boots make with each step.

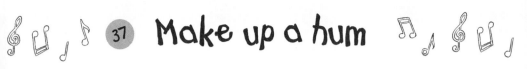

37 Make up a hum

Pooh often hums when he is thinking or if he's trying to make sense of something. Your own hum can be about anything you like – what you'd like for dinner, what the weather's like or what you did this morning. It might rhyme and it might use some made-up words, there are no rules.

The more it snows
(Tiddely pom),
The more it goes
(Tiddely pom),
The more it goes
(Tiddely pom),
On snowing.

And nobody knows
(Tiddely pom),
How cold my toes
(Tiddely pom),
How cold my toes
(Tiddely pom),
Are growing.

38 Cress growing

You will need:

* 1 egg
* cress seeds
* cotton wool
* felt-tip pens
* water

1 Break the top of your egg shell with a teaspoon.

2 Empty the egg and rinse out the shell – be very careful as this can be fiddly!

3 Draw a funny face on the egg with your felt tip pens.

4 Place wet kitchen roll in the bottom of your egg and damp cotton wool on top.

5 Sprinkle your cress seeds and keep your egg in a warm place with some sunlight.

6 After about 7 days, you should see shoots appear.

Cress is especially yummy in egg sandwiches!

39 Stargazing

Look up into the sky at night and count as many stars as you can. Notice if they're bright or very faint. Can you see the moon? If you can, is it a full circle or a crescent shape?

The Plough
(Big Dipper)

Hint: Look out for the man in the moon!

Little Bear

NORTH STAR

Groups of stars are called constellations.
Some of these constellations are named after the
shapes they make. Take a look at the constellations
here and see if you can find them in the sky.

40 Make a sundial

To build your sundial, you will need a long stick or branch. You will also need 12 pebbles or stones, for your hour marks.

Get everything ready for 12 o'clock, when the sun is high in the sky. Using a spoon, dig a deep hole in the ground, just wider than your stick. Make sure you have space around the hole for your hour markers. Put your branch or stick in the hole and fill it in with soil. Where the stick makes a shadow on the ground is your 12 o'clock, place your biggest stone here.

On every hour until bed time, check where the stick's shadow has got to and add another pebble to your sundial. Do this until 6pm and start at 7 o'clock the next morning, until your dial is complete!

Daring challenges

Christopher Robin was sitting outside his door, putting on his **Big Boots.** As soon as he saw the Big Boots, Pooh knew that an Adventure was going to happen.

41 Stepping stones

Stepping stones are often found in streams or shallow water. Be sure to check that the stones are stable before you step onto them and ask for a grown-up's help.

Once you feel safe on your stepping stone, have a look at the stream or brook you are crossing.

Can you see under the water? Are there any fish, or maybe frogs?

42 Walk the tightrope

Circus performers who walk along thin wire high in the sky are called tightrope walkers.

Try tightrope walking on the edge of pavements or low walls in the park. Always hold the hand of a grown-up and walk very slowly in a straight line.

Imagine that you are at the top of a circus tent and the crowd is cheering you on. Or you could imagine you are high in the sky and invent what you can see below. Are you walking high up above the desert, on the wing of an aeroplane, or across the ocean?

43 Poohsticks

With the help of an adult, find a bridge that goes over water.

Choose a stick each and line up on one side of the bridge. All let go of your sticks at the same time.

Now, quickly go to the other side of the bridge and watch to see whose stick makes it out first.

The first stick to appear is the winner!

And that was the beginning of the game called Poohsticks,
which Pooh invented, and which he and his friends
used to play on the edge of the Forest.

44 Build a den

To build your own explorer's den, try running a washing line or cord between two posts, tree trunks or chairs. Put your sheet over the frame and drape 2/3 over one side and 1/3 over the other so your den has a door.

Or instead you could try making a den of sticks. Stack them up, just like Eeyore.

You will need an adult's help.

Fill your den with cushions and blankets and you have the perfect place to hang out. You can prete a safari tent that is su imals or you could on th ready to land

Alexandra's Favorite

'We've finished our House ...'
sang the gruff voice.
'Tiddely Pom!' sang the squeaky one.
'It's a beautiful HOUSE ...'
'Tiddely Pom ...'
'I wish it were MINE ...'
'Tiddely Pom ...'

45 Fly a kite

To make your kite you will need:

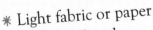

* Light fabric or paper
* Wooden dowel
* Sticky tape
* Scissors
* String (2 metres long)

You will need a wide open space away from roads, trees or power lines.

Make a cross with the dowels and secure together with string.

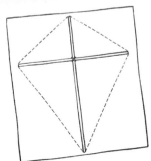

 Lay the cross on fabric or paper and draw a diamond shape around.

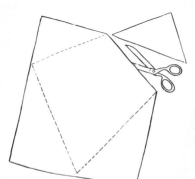

 Cut out diamond (ask a grown-up to help).

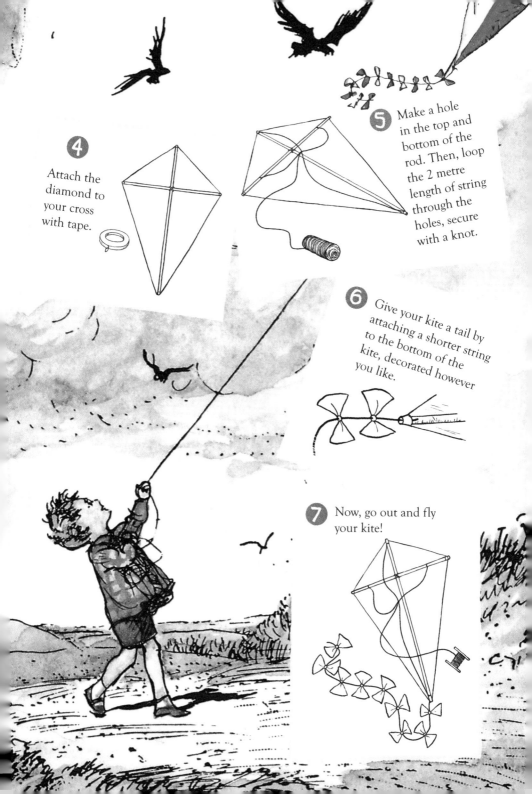

4 Attach the diamond to your cross with tape.

5 Make a hole in the top and bottom of the rod. Then, loop the 2 metre length of string through the holes, secure with a knot.

6 Give your kite a tail by attaching a shorter string to the bottom of the kite, decorated however you like.

7 Now, go out and fly your kite!

46

Moonlit wander

Sometimes, the places we visit most in the day can look completely different at night. Take a walk down the road that you live on, or just tiptoe into your back garden and notice how different everything seems (take a grown-up with you). Notice the sounds, shapes and colours. You may hear sounds you aren't used to, like owls or foxes. Does it feel exciting, or scary, or peaceful?

47 Look at the world from a tree branch

Find a tree with strong-looking branches so that you can get a good hold as you climb. Take it slowly and keep looking up for anything that might get in the way.

Once you've safely reached your branch, look around at the view. How much more can you see up here than on the ground?

You will need an adult's help.

48 Water fight

On a hot day, a water fight is the perfect game to play to stay cool. You need open space and an outdoor tap or hose.

Fill up buckets, plastic tubs and water balloons and divide into teams. If you like, time your game in rounds – everyone has five minutes to throw as much water as they can and then time to rest and dry off.

Ask an adult for permission.

Be careful of slippery surfaces when you've been playing with water.

49 Build a snowman

The best snowmen are made from light, fluffy snow that has just fallen. Make a snowball by packing a handful of snow together. Keep adding handfuls and roll it along the ground until it's about 30cm tall. Repeat this step to make three snowballs in total. Stack the snowballs on top of each other. Use more snow to pack in between the layers.

Add pebbles or buttons for eyes, a smile and a carrot for a nose. Use sticks for arms and accessorise with an old scarf and a hat!

Don't forget to take a picture of your snowman to stick at the back of this book.

 Camp out

It's time to put all of your wilderness exploring to good use and hold your own overnight camp-out.

marshmallows

torch

sleeping bag

tent

biscuits

mat

You will need a sleeping bag, a camping mat or yoga mat, a tent (or make the den from page 56), marshmallows, digestive biscuits, tea-lights (for adults only), a torch or glow sticks. You can camp in your garden or, if you want to be really adventurous, in a forest near home. Invite your friends and always camp out with an adult.

While it's light, set up your shelter with the help of an adult and place blankets and pillows inside.

You will need an adult's help.

When it starts to get dark, thread your marshmallows onto wooden skewers and hold them over a flame until they start to melt (get an adult to help you). Once the marshmallow turns gooey and goes a light brown colour on the outside, sandwich it between two digestive biscuits and you'll have delicious s'mores!

Turn the page for more fun camping activities!

When it's dark make shadows using your torch and the silhouette activity on pages 21 and 70 of this book.

Use glow sticks for light and make patterns as you wave them around.

When it's time for bed, close up your tent and bury underneath your blankets so you're as snug as a bug!

Take a look at the stars and find the shapes mentioned on pages 48 and 49.

Take turns telling stories and singing songs.

How did you do?

Now you've tried lots of new things,
fill in this page to keep memories
of all your adventures.

I got very messy during this activity:

I was given this
book by:

Something I tried for the
first time was:

I think the most adventurous
activity was:

The activity I most
enjoyed was:

The hardest activity
for me was:

The biggest bug I saw was:

Shadow puppets

You can copy or trace the shapes on this page and use them for the activity on page 21.

Forest facts

Forests keep us alive! Trees help us to breathe by changing carbon dioxide, a chemical we breathe out, into oxygen which we need to breathe in. Without trees and plants, we would not have enough oxygen to breathe.

The tallest tree in the world is nearly 116 metres tall – that's about as tall as 23 giraffes!

Most trees' leaves turn brown or red in the autumn, fall off in winter and grow back in spring. But evergreen trees, such as pine trees, never lose their leaves.

The biggest animal which lives in trees is the orangutan.

The widest tree trunk in the world has a circumference (the distance around the outside of the trunk) of 42 metres. It would take about 24 people holding hands to reach around the trunk.

The oldest tree is in Sweden and it's about 9550 years old!

Winnie-the-Pooh and his friends live in The Hundred Acre Wood, which is actually based on Ashdown Forest, in East Sussex, where A.A.Milne lived with his son, Christopher Robin.

Gallery

Stick photos of your adventures here:

Get creative

Use this page for your doodles and drawings:

Explorer notes

Make your wilderness explorer notes here:

Index